alto
sax

Now you c[...]
alto saxoph[...]
specially rec[...] [...]ments

TV THEMES

TAKE THE LEAD

alto saxophone

IMP

International
MUSIC
Publications

International Music Publications Limited
Griffin House 161 Hammersmith Road London W6 8BS England

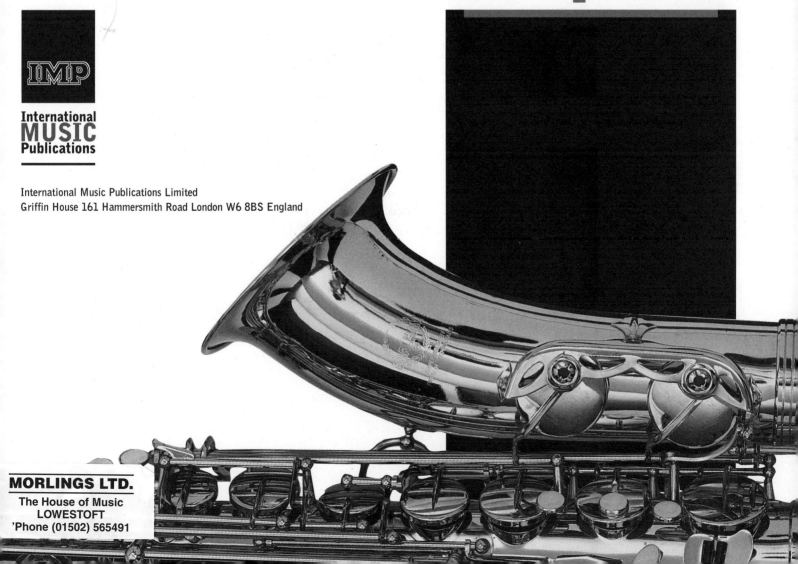

Series Editor: Sadie Cook

Editorial, production and recording: Artemis Music Limited
Design & Production: Space DPS Limited

Published 1999

International
MUSIC
Publications

International Music Publications Limited
Griffin House 161 Hammersmith Road London W6 8BS England

International Music Publications Limited

England: Griffin House
               161 Hammersmith Road
               London W6 8BS

Germany: Marstallstr. 8
               D-80539 München

Denmark: Danmusik
               Vognmagergade 7
               DK1120 Copenhagen K

Carisch

Italy: Via Campania 12
               20098 San Giuliano Milanese
               Milano

Spain: Magallanes 25
               28015 Madrid

France: 20 Rue de la Ville-l'Eveque
               75008 Paris

alto saxophone

TAKE THE LEAD

In the Book...

On the CD...

Coronation Street

Demonstration

Backing

By Eric Spear

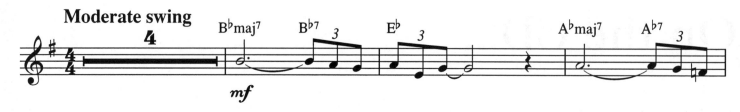

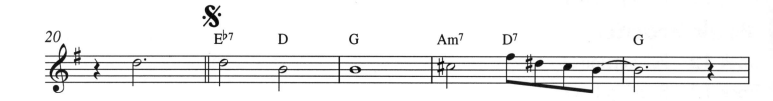

I'll Be There For You

(theme from *Friends*)

Words and Music by
Phil Solem, Marta Kauffman, David Crane,
Michael Skloff, Allee Willis and Danny Wilde

Demonstration Backing

Match Of The Day

Demonstration   Backing

By Rhet Stoller

(Meet) The Flintstones

Demonstration   Backing

Words and Music by Joseph Barbera,
William Hanna and Hoyt Curtain

15

Men Behaving Badly

Demonstration

Backing

By Alan Lisk

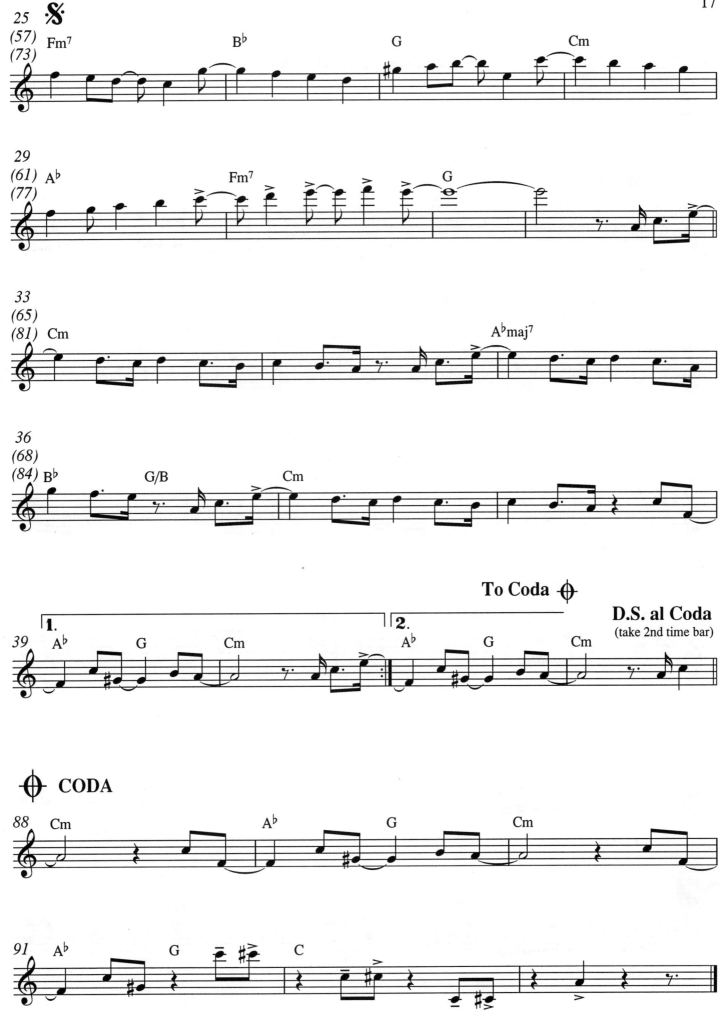

Demonstration   Backing

Peak Practice

By John Altman

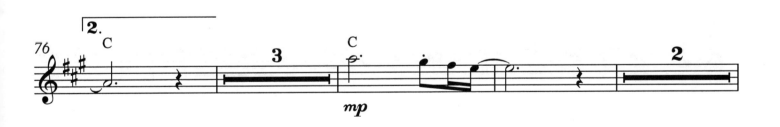

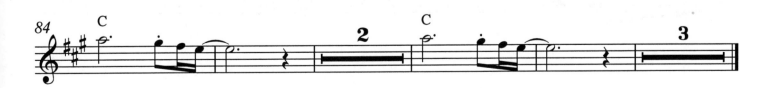

The Simpsons

Demonstration

Backing

By Danny Elfman

Rather fast

Demonstration

Backing

The X-Files

By Mark Snow

Printed by
Halstan & Co. Ltd., Amersham, Bucks., England

You can be the featured soloist with
TAKE THE LEAD

Collect these titles, each with demonstration and full backing tracks on CD.

90s Hits	Movie Hits	TV Themes	Christmas Songs
The Air That I Breathe (Simply Red)	**Because You Loved Me** (Up Close And Personal)	**Coronation Street**	**The Christmas Song (Chestnuts Roasting On An Open Fire)**
Angels (Robbie Williams)	**Blue Monday** (The Wedding Singer)	**I'll Be There For You (theme from Friends)**	**Frosty The Snowman**
How Do I Live (LeAnn Rimes)	**(Everything I Do) I Do It For You** (Robin Hood: Prince Of Thieves)	**Match Of The Day**	**Have Yourself A Merry Little Christmas**
I Don't Want To Miss A Thing (Aerosmith)	**I Don't Want To Miss A Thing** (Armageddon)	**(Meet) The Flintstones**	**Little Donkey**
I'll Be There For You (The Rembrandts)	**I Will Always Love You** (The Bodyguard)	**Men Behaving Badly**	**Rudolph The Red-Nosed Reindeer**
My Heart Will Go On (Celine Dion)	**Star Wars (Main Title)** (Star Wars)	**Peak Practice**	**Santa Claus Is Comin' To Town**
Something About The Way You Look Tonight (Elton John)	**The Wind Beneath My Wings** (Beaches)	**The Simpsons**	**Sleigh Ride**
Frozen (Madonna)	**You Can Leave Your Hat On** (The Full Monty)	**The X-Files**	**Winter Wonderland**

Order ref: 6725A – Flute	Order ref: 6908A – Flute	Order ref: 7003A – Flute	Order ref: 7022A – Flute
Order ref: 6726A – Clarinet	Order ref: 6909A – Clarinet	Order ref: 7004A – Clarinet	Order ref: 7023A – Clarinet
Order ref: 6727A – Alto Saxophone	Order ref: 6910A – Alto Saxophone	Order ref: 7005A – Alto Saxophone	Order ref: 7024A – Alto Saxophone
Order ref: 6728A – Violin	Order ref: 6911A – Tenor Saxophone	Order ref: 7006A – Violin	Order ref: 7025A – Violin
	Order ref: 6912A – Violin		Order ref: 7026A – Piano
			Order ref: 7027A – Drums